BE A SUPER TEST-TAKER

LEVEL E-F

A Program to Help Today's Young People with Today's Tests

Gervasi

Scholastic, Inc.

Senior Vice President, Director of Education: Dr. Ernest Fleishman
Editor in Chief: Catherine Vanderhoof
Managing Editor: Sandy Kelley

Created and developed by The Learning Source
Consultants: Dr. Richard Antes, Department of Counseling, Indiana State University;
Dr. Gloria Maccow, Department of Psychology, Illinois State University

Vice President, Director, Editorial Design and Production: Will Kefauver
Art Director: Joan Michael
Designer: Krystina J. Mankowski
Cover: Phil Perry
Illustrator: Krystina J. Mankowski
Editorial Production Director: Richard Walsh
Assistant Production Director: Bryan Samolinski
Production Editor: Danny Cohen
Production/Design Support: Leslie Joyce, Adam Yellin

Acknowledgments:
pp.20-21: From *Secrets of a Summer Spy* by Janice Jones. Copyright © 1990 by Janice L. Jones. Used by
permission of Bradbury Press; p.22: From *My Brother, My Sister, and I* by Yoko Kawashima Watkins.
Copyright © 1994 by Yoko Kawashima Watkins. Used by permission of Bradbury Press; p.24: From *Shark
Beneath the Reef* by Jean Craighead George. Copyright © 1989 by Jean Craighead George. Reprinted by
permission of HarperCollins Publishers; p.26: From *The Hideout* by Sigrid Heuck, translation copyright
© 1988 by Rika Lesser, Copyright © 1986 by Sigrid Heuck. Used by permission of Dutton Signet, a division
of Penguin Books USA Inc.; p.28: From *What's Down There? Questions and Answers About the Ocean* by Dinah
Moche. Copyright © 1984 by Dinah Moche. Reprinted by permission of Scholastic Inc.; p.29: From
Helicopter Pilots by Nancy J. Nielsen. Copyright © 1988 by Crestwood House Inc. Used by permission;
p.30: From *Boundary Waters Canoe Area Minnesota* by Nancy J. Nielsen. Copyright © 1989 by Crestwood
House. Used by permission; p.31: From *The China Clipper* by Peter Guttmacher. Copyright © 1994 by
Crestwood House. Used by permission.

6 7 8 9 10 14 99

HOW THIS BOOK CAN HELP YOU

It's the day of the test. Your mind is wandering, your stomach hurts, and your hands are trembling. Does this sound familiar?

Relax. You're not alone. Almost everyone feels nervous before a test. *Be a Super Test-Taker* can help you feel more comfortable and confident when taking tests. Here's how:

In this book you will learn about different kinds of tests. This includes multiple-choice tests, short-answer tests, and long-answer or open-ended tests.

You will also learn how to:

- Find key words in directions.
- Mark your answers.
- Check your work.
- Eliminate incorrect choices.
- Use your time well.

As you work through the book, you will discover what you may or may not know about tests. Identifying your strengths and weaknesses will help you understand which test-taking skills you need to improve the most.

There are lots of practice test items in this book that will help prepare you for items on a real test. They will also teach you to pace yourself during a test. Correct pacing will help you to answer every question, even when you need time to think about the harder ones. As a result, you will be confident that you are doing your very best!

By the time you finish the book, you will be ready to earn the best test score you can. You will also be able to face tests without sweaty hands and an upset stomach, knowing that you are prepared to take on any type of test that comes your way.

Table of

Contents

UNIT: ▶ 1 LEARNING ABOUT TESTS

RECOGNIZING DIFFERENT TYPES OF TESTS

Exploring Test Formats

There are three main kinds of tests:

    multiple-choice

    short-answer

    long-answer

Each kind of test asks you to complete special tasks, using different test-taking skills. Let's explore the different test formats and learn some ways to approach each type of test.

Multiple-Choice Tests

In multiple-choice tests, each item has three or four answer choices. Usually one response for each test item is correct. You have to choose the one best response and fill in the oval that goes with it.

This is what a multiple-choice item may look like:

Another word for <u>picture</u> is

  ◯ a. frame.   ⬤ c. illustration.

  ◯ b. proven.   ◯ d. pitcher.

Since *illustration* is a synonym (another word) for *picture,* the oval in front of *illustration* has been filled in.

Sometimes **more than one response** is correct. If this is the case, the directions will clearly tell you that there may be several correct answers.

Antonym Tests

Some multiple-choice vocabulary tests ask you to find **antonyms.** Antonyms are words that mean the opposite or almost the opposite of the test word in a phrase.

To find the correct response, first read the phrase and all the answer choices. Quickly eliminate the ones that you know are definitely wrong. Then, in your own words, try to define for yourself the underlined word and the remaining choices before you make your response.

Here is an example:

a <u>reckless</u> person

  ◯ a. careful   ◯ c. dangerous

  ◯ b. curious   ◯ d. charming

Reckless means *careless,* and the opposite of *careless* is *careful.* So the correct answer is *a. careful.*

Try It Yourself

Fill in the oval beside the antonym for each underlined word.

1. peaceful afternoon
- ○ a. happy ○ b. exciting ○ c. relaxing ○ d. summer

2. grim person
- ○ a. happy ○ b. moody ○ c. caring ○ d. sick

3. resent those comments
- ○ a. enjoy ○ b. heard ○ c. said ○ d. hate

4. primitive creature
- ○ a. odd ○ b. tall ○ c. ugly ○ d. modern

Analogy Tests

Analogies are another common type of multiple-choice test. They ask you to compare two pairs of words and show the relationship between them. Here is an example:

pen : writer :: hammer : ?
- ○ a. police officer ○ c. truck driver
- ○ b. carpenter ○ d. NG

The right answer is *b. carpenter*. A pen is a tool used by a writer, just as a hammer is a tool used by a carpenter.

Hint

A simple way to figure out an analogy is to substitute the phrase *is to* (or *are to*) for the single colons (:) and substitute *as* for the double colons (::). Then the analogy reads like this: Pen is to writer as hammer is to carpenter.

SUPER TEST-TAKER Tip:
WHEN THE CORRECT RESPONSE IS NOT GIVEN

Some multiple-choice tests include a special oval to mark if the answer is not given. This oval may say NG (for Not Given), NH (for Not Here), or None of the Above. Mark this oval if the correct response is not among the other choices.

Try It Yourself

Read the analogy. Then choose the best answer by filling in the oval next to your answer choice.

5. judge : courtroom :: scientist :
- ○ a. market ○ b. laboratory ○ c. cockpit ○ d. NG

6. sparrow : bird :: cobra :
- ○ a. cat ○ b. dog ○ c. horse ○ d. NG

7. crying : sadness :: laughter :
- ○ a. joy ○ b. fear ○ c. calm ○ d. NG

8. chimney : house :: steeple :
- ○ a. cabin ○ b. church ○ c. trailer ○ d. NG

Short-Answer Tests

For short-answer tests, you may be asked to write your answers in numbers, letters, words, or sentences. Sometimes you will be asked to gather information from a map, schedule, or graph. At other times you will have to use information from a reading selection to get the answer. No matter what the test is like, always read the directions carefully to find out exactly what you have to write on the answer sheet.

Try It Yourself

Read the items and write the correct response in the space provided. Use the empty space on this page to show your work.

For example, a short-answer math test may ask you to solve problems and write the answers in the spaces provided. A sample question would look like this.

• 59 – 43 + 21 = _____

First you would work out the problem where you are told, usually either in a work space on the test page or on scratch paper. Then you would write the response, which is 37, in the space.

---

9. 16 + 23 + 27 = _____

10. 1.83 – .37 – .26 = _____

11. 13 x 5 = _____

12. 124 x 13 = _____

13. 569 + 931 + 1269 = _____

14. 9.5 + 0.03 + .02 + 1.16 = _____

Long-Answer Tests

There are many different types of long-answer tests. Some ask you to answer questions in sentences. Others ask for some kind of extended writing, such as an essay or personal response. (In Unit 2 you will find specific information about tests that ask you to do writing.)

Sometimes a test checks your knowledge and skills by asking you to do a project. You may be asked to create a travel plan, a TV show, a news report, a map, a model, or a scientific experiment. This type of test allows you to use both your knowledge and imagination. But it also requires a great deal of thought.

For example, a project may give you a budget of $100 and ask you to plan a two-hour party. A band costs $40 an hour. A DJ costs $25 an hour. One can of soda for each of your guests totals $10. One bag of chips for each guest totals $10. How would you spend your budget? In this kind of test, you would have to explain how you decided.

In project tests, there is usually more than one correct response. For the two-hour party, for example, you could choose to hire the band for the whole party and buy one bag of chips and one can of soda for each guest. Or you could choose the DJ, two bags of chips, and three cans of soda for each guest. The most important thing is that you explain how you arrived at your response and check to see that your calculations are correct.

Some project tests tell you to work in a group. When you are working with others, it is important for everyone to work together well. Here are some tips to remember:

- Make sure everyone has a chance to give their ideas.
- Concentrate on the task you are given. Don't waste time fooling around or arguing.
- No one should say anything to hurt or put down other group members.
- Everyone should have a say in group discussions.
- With any type of long-answer test, read the directions carefully so that you know exactly what type of response or responses you are expected to give.
- Do all parts of the project.
- Make sure you know how much time you have to work.

Try It Yourself

You have 40 minutes to complete this project. Be sure to read all the instructions before you start to work.

15. Your school photography club needs new equipment. The total cost of the enlarger, tripod, and photo paper you need is $300.00. Work with two other people to plan a sale to raise funds for the club.

Your school has given you space in the gym for your sale. You can have that space for one hour after school on Friday or for three hours on Saturday morning. You estimate that twice as many people will come to your sale on Friday as on Saturday.

If you have your sale on Saturday, you can sell pancake breakfasts for $3.00 each. If you have your sale on Friday, you can sell baked goods for $1.00 apiece.

a. To make sure you are selling enough to make your goal at the end of the sale, you need to monitor your average sales every 10 minutes. How many sales will you need to make during each 10-minute period on Friday?

_____

b. About how many sales will you need to make during each 10-minute period on Saturday?

_____

c. When will you have your sale? Explain how you decided.

_____

_____

_____

_____

_____

More help for taking multiple-choice, short-answer, and long-answer tests will be provided in the strategies sections of this unit.

FOLLOWING TEST DIRECTIONS

Test directions explain what you have to do on a test. Carefully reading and following test directions will help you do your best on any test.

No matter what a test asks you to do, always follow these five steps:

- Listen to your teacher's instructions carefully.
- Read all the directions. Don't assume you know how to do it.
- Say the directions to yourself in your own words.
- Make sure you understand what you have to do.
- Ask questions if you need to **before** the test begins.

Finding the Key Words in Directions

The key words in directions are the most important words. They explain what you have to do on a particular test. Look for action words. Here are some key action words that are often used in test directions:

read	fill in	choose	circle
mark	pick	solve	write

Position words are also important. Here are some of the ones you will see quite often:

next to	above	before
in front of	below	after

Try It Yourself

Underline the key words in the following directions.

Ex.: <u>Write</u> your answer <u>on the line</u>.

16. Fill in the circle next to your answer choice.

17. Choose the best answer for each question.

18. Read the question. Then write in the best answer.

19. Solve the following problems.

20. Write your answer in the box below.

Following Multistep Directions

Sometimes test directions will instruct you to do one task, such as filling in part of a sentence, finding a sum, or naming a capital city.

Other times, the directions will instruct you to complete several steps. For instance, a language-arts test might ask you to read a story and then answer questions about it. A math test might ask you to add some numbers and subtract the sum from a larger number.

Hint

- Make sure you understand all the steps you are asked to do.
- Complete each step of the process the way the directions tell you to.
- Keep working steadily until you have finished or the time is up. Don't let worrying that you won't finish keep you from doing as much as you can!

Try It Yourself

Read the following fable. Then complete the items on the following page. After you have finished, provide a moral for the fable.

The Hare and the Hound

One day a hound, out hunting by himself, flushed a hare from a thicket and gave chase. The frightened hare gave the dog a long run and escaped. As the disappointed hound turned back toward home, a passing goatherd said jeeringly: "You are a fine hunter! Aren't you ashamed to let a little hare one-tenth your size get the best of you?"

"You forget," replied the hound, "that I was only running for my supper, but the hare was running for his life!"

Remember

The *moral* of a fable or tale is the lesson that it teaches.

21. A hound is a _____.
◯ a. person   ◯ b. dog   ◯ c. horse   ◯ d. rabbit

22. Which of these happened in the fable?
◯ a. The hare outran the hound.   ◯ c. The hound caught the hare.
◯ b. The hound killed the hare.   ◯ d. The goatherd killed the hare.

23. What is the moral of the fable?

_____

_____

Now solve these multistep math problems.
Write your answers in the space provided.
Show your work in the space to the right.

24. Hallie has $12.00. Her brother Ben has $13.50. They want to buy a video game that costs $55.00.

a. How much more money do they need?

_____

b. How long will it be before they can buy the game if each of them earns $5.00 per week?

_____

25. The Morton family is taking a trip to visit some relatives. The first part of their journey—to their grandparents' house—is 125 miles. The second leg—to their cousins' house—is 97 miles. The third leg of the trip—to their aunt's house—is 153 miles.

a. How far will they travel to see all their relatives?

_____

b. How long will the whole trip be if they must travel another 120 miles to get home again?

_____

STRATEGIES FOR MULTIPLE-CHOICE ITEMS

You have found out that there are three different kinds of tests: multiple-choice, short-answer, and long-answer. In the sections that follow, you will learn more that will help you with each kind of test. You will also get practice that will make you as test-wise as you can possibly be.

Taking Multiple-Choice Tests

Multiple-choice test items call for special test-taking skills. To do your best, follow these steps:

- If you have any questions about what you are supposed to do, ask them **before** the test begins.
- Read the directions and the test items completely.
- Read **all** the choices before you mark your answer.
- Mark your answer the way the directions tell you to.
- If you are not sure of an answer, skip the question. Return to it after you have answered all the others.

SUPER TEST-TAKER TIP: CHANGING A MULTIPLE-CHOICE ANSWER

To change a multiple-choice response, erase the old response completely. Don't just cross it out. Then fill in the new oval.

Trying Out and Eliminating Choices

You can save time on multiple-choice tests by trying out and eliminating choices. How can you eliminate wrong responses quickly? Follow these steps:

- For math tests, estimate or work out your response first. For other tests, think of what the response should be. Say your response in your head.
- Compare your response with the choices.
- If you can't find a response that matches yours, check your work.
- If you still can't find the response, check NG if it is a choice. If not, work the problem again.

Try It Yourself

Read all the choices. Then fill in the best response.

---

26. What is the next number in the pattern?

3, 9, 27, 81, [ ]

○ a. 243   ○ c. 600
○ b. 96   ○ d. 3

27. What is the next number in the pattern?

2,500, 500, 100, 20, [ ]

○ a. 3   ○ c. 5
○ b. 4   ○ d. 8,000

28. What is the missing number in the pattern?

12, 48, 192, [ ], 3,072

○ a. 216   ○ c. 324
○ b. 678   ○ d. 768

29. What is the missing number in the pattern?

3, 10, 17, 24, 31, [ ], 45

○ a. 32   ○ c. 38
○ b. 35   ○ d. 44

Synonyms

Some vocabulary tests ask you to find synonyms. These are words that mean the same, or almost the same, as the test word in a phrase. All the answer choices may make sense in the phrase. But only one choice is a synonym and, therefore, correct.

Try It Yourself

Read all the choices. Then eliminate the wrong choices and fill in the oval beside the synonym of the underlined word.

30. <u>expand</u> your knowledge
◯ a. ruin ◯ b. lose ◯ c. use ◯ d. increase

31. <u>mischievous</u> grin
◯ a. naughty ◯ b. nice ◯ c. eager ◯ d. pitiful

32. useful <u>gadget</u>
◯ a. game ◯ b. name ◯ c. style ◯ d. tool

33. <u>shrewd</u> businessman
◯ a. rich ◯ b. clever ◯ c. foolish ◯ d. honest

34. <u>vivid</u> image
◯ a. clear ◯ b. absent ◯ c. pleasant ◯ d. great

35. <u>menace</u> to society
◯ a. gift ◯ b. danger ◯ c. pleasure ◯ d. inspiration

36. <u>recite</u> poetry
◯ a. say ◯ b. write ◯ c. hear ◯ d. want

37. <u>estimate</u> the cost
◯ a. learn ◯ b. guess ◯ c. hear ◯ d. read

STRATEGIES FOR SHORT-ANSWER ITEMS

Tests with short-answer items call for different strategies from those used for multiple-choice tests. Follow these steps to make sure you do your best when taking short-answer tests.

- If you have questions about the test, ask them **before** the test begins.

- Read the directions and the test items completely.

- Before you write, say your response in your head to see if it makes sense.

- Write your response in the correct place on the answer sheet.

- Reread your response and check to make sure that it is correct.

Preparation and Organization

How else can you be sure to do your best on short-answer tests? You can prepare and organize!

Prepare

- Study the material you need to know for the test.

- Get enough sleep the night before the test. Be sure to eat a healthy breakfast.

- Bring the materials you need, such as pencils, pens, and paper.

Organize

- Organize your test materials and writing tools so you can find everything you need fast.

- Answer the easiest questions first. Answer the hardest ones last. That way, you'll be less likely to run out of time.

Using Information from a Passage

Sometimes you will be asked to write short answers to questions about a reading passage you are given in the test. The responses will come from information in the passage. You may be asked for:

- a fact stated in the passage

- an idea you infer, or figure out, from clues in the selection and what you already know

- your own opinion, based on facts in the passage

Read the passage first. Then read each question. Go back and scan the passage to look for specific facts. When you scan, you run your eyes over a passage looking for specific words and phrases.

Try It Yourself

Read the passage and items 38-42. Then write in the best response for each item. The first one is done for you.

Hardscrabble was one of the quietest places in the world. The only sounds were the whisper of a brook or the whistle of a bird. It was in the deep valleys of southern Pennsylvania. A sleepy, dreamy feeling seemed to hang over the land, even today.

The people of Hardscrabble were the great-grandchildren of the German settlers who had come to Pennsylvania in the 1600s. René Epinard, a teacher, wanted to be the mayor of Hardscrabble. He was not German, like his neighbors. He had come from France. Unlike the tall Germans, Epinard was short and stout. His feet and hands were small; his head was bald. He spent a lot of his time alone.

Ex.: Where does the story take place?

Hardscrabble, Pennsylvania

38. What is the origin of most of the people of this town?

_____

39. Who is René Epinard?

_____

40. How is René Epinard different from his neighbors?

_____

_____

41. How do you think the people of the town feel about René Epinard?

_____

_____

42. What do you think the rest of the story will be about?

_____

_____

STRATEGIES FOR LONG-ANSWER TESTS

Managing your time well is one of the most important parts of taking tests that ask for long responses. Whether you are asked to complete a project or do a piece of writing, you need to plan how you will use your time and keep track of the time as you work.

When a test asks you to do a project, it will ask you to work either by yourself or with a group. Since you are often asked to do a lot of different tasks on these tests, it is very important to keep track of what needs to be done and to check your work carefully. Outline or list the different tasks you are asked to do. Then check them off as you do them.

When tests ask you for a piece of writing, make sure you understand exactly what type of writing you are being asked to do. (Unit 2 will give you help with writing.)

Checking Long-Answer Items

As you reread your responses on any long-answer test, make sure you:

- responded to the item you were asked about
- gave a complete response
- explained your response fully
- wrote neatly and clearly
- wrote in the correct place on the test or answer sheet
- spelled all words correctly
- used the right punctuation

Checking Projects

Projects may include speaking, performing, building, or drawing, along with writing and math. Since there are so many different parts to most projects, these tests must be checked carefully.

To check a project, see if you:

- completed every part of the project
- labeled all parts with your name and class
- handed in all the different parts of the project

Try It Yourself

Read the directions and the map on page 19 carefully. Then answer the questions that follow.

43. In what town is the restaurant?

_____

44. About how far did Nick have to travel?

_____

45. Create a set of directions telling someone how to get to Brooktown from the airport. Include direction words like *north* and *east;* position words like *right* and *left;* and landmarks like lakes and railroad tracks.

_____

_____

_____

_____

_____

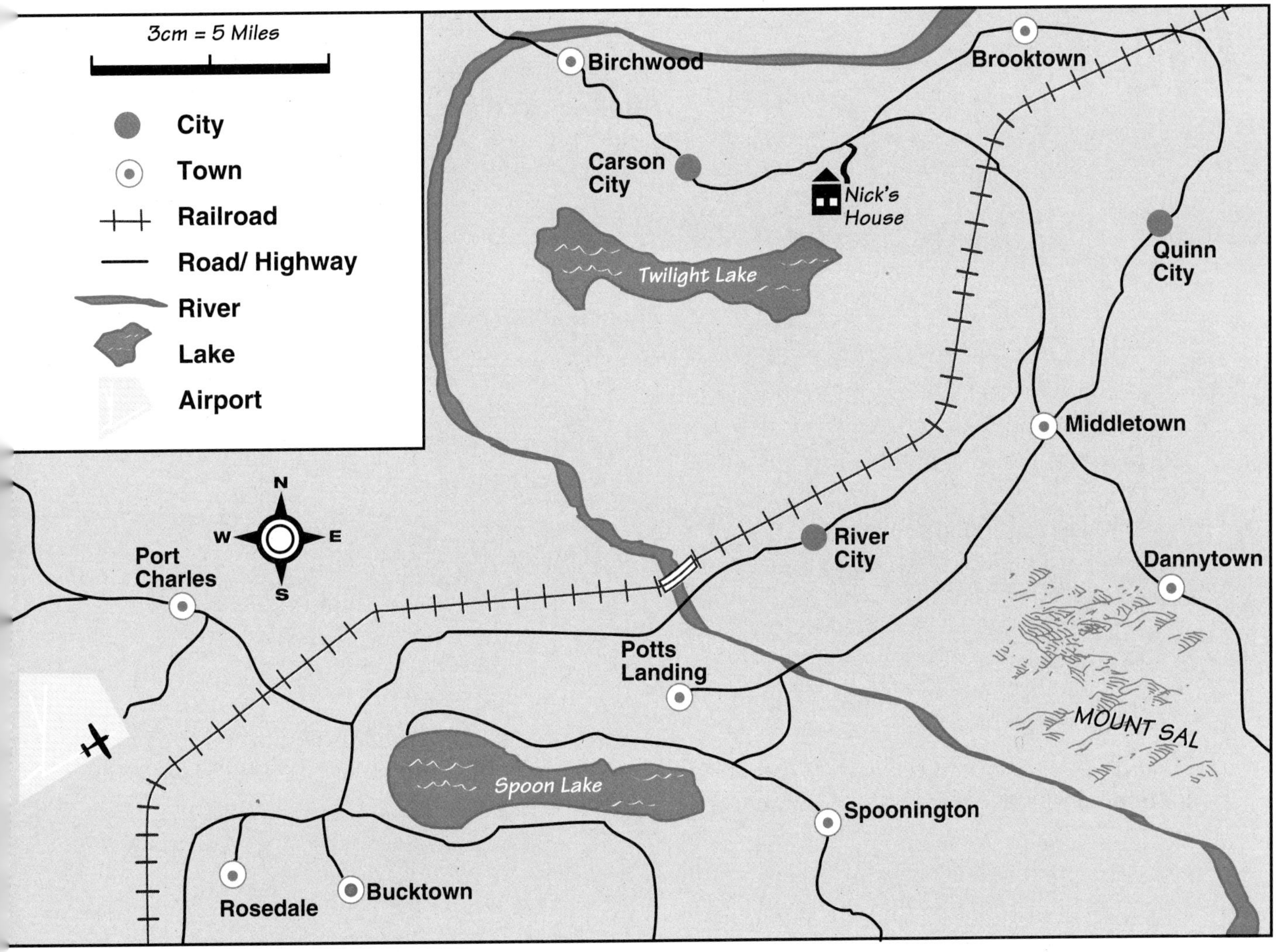
3cm = 5 Miles
City
Town
Railroad
Road/ Highway
River
Lake
Airport
N
W
E
S
Birchwood
Brooktown
Carson City
Nick's House
Quinn City
Twilight Lake
Middletown
Port Charles
River City
Dannytown
Potts Landing
MOUNT SAL
Spoon Lake
Spoonington
Rosedale
Bucktown

Pete calls his friend Nick and invites him out to dinner. He tells Nick that the address of the restaurant is 199 Main Street. Pete gives Nick the following directions.

- Make a right turn at your driveway.
- Bear right at the fork.
- Make the first right turn after crossing the railroad tracks.
- Drive across the river and, at the next fork, bear left.
- Turn right and go west. Take your second left and drive south into town.

UNIT: 2 TESTS ABOUT READING AND WRITING

READING FICTION

Reading tests ask many different kinds of questions about story selections. These questions can be in multiple-choice, short-answer, or long-answer form. They may check your knowledge of words and of the elements of fiction, like plot, setting, and character. They may also test your comprehension skills by checking how well you understand details, summarize, or draw conclusions from story selections.

Understanding Words

Some tests ask you to read a passage and find synonyms for one or more words in that passage.

Here is an example. Read the passage and the item that follows.

> Amy Parrish, Jimmy Jackman, and I had spent our summers together on Harbor Island for as long as we could remember. Jimmy and I lived on the island year-round, but Amy and her parents only came to northern Michigan when school was out. The Parrishes lived four hours away by car in Detroit, where Amy's parents taught school. Mr. Parrish loved to fish, and Amy's mom liked to sketch by the lake, so a summer cottage on Harbor Island kept everyone happy.

• In this passage, the word <u>sketch</u> (line 11) means _____.

  ◯ a. skate   ◯ c. stretch
  ◯ b. draw   ◯ d. pencils

Look back at line 11 in the selection for the word *sketch*. From the passage, we know that the word will be an activity that someone would enjoy doing during the summer. To sketch usually means "to draw." Now look among the answer choices. Is the word *draw* there? When you find it, mark the correct oval, *b. draw*.

Try It Yourself

Fill in the oval next to the response that means the same or almost the same as the word in the selection.

1. In this selection, the word *cottage* (line 12) means _____.

  ◯ a. vacation   ◯ c. house
  ◯ b. journey   ◯ d. cheese

2. In this selection, the word *year-round* (line 5) means _____.

  ◯ a. in a circle   ◯ c. all year
  ◯ b. each summer   ◯ d. for many years

Try It Yourself

Now read this selection and fill in the oval next to the correct synonyms below.

My stomach did a flip-flop, and I stood rooted to the spot, unable to make up my mind. Should I go in or take off running? Then I remembered how Jimmy said I was the bravest girl he knew. And how Amy had tricked him into walking her home, leaving me standing alone on the beach. Amy would never be daring enough to go into the old cat-lady's house, I reasoned. Here was my chance to impress Jimmy, and I was going to take it. I stepped up on the porch and walked past Mrs. Peet into the kitchen.

3. In the selection, the word *rooted* (line 1) means _____.

◯ a. cheering ◯ b. wobbly ◯ c. underground ◯ d. fixed

4. In the selection, the word *impress* (line 7) means _____.

◯ a. influence ◯ b. ignore ◯ c. see ◯ d. find

5. In the selection, the word *daring* (line 5) means _____.

◯ a. lazy ◯ b. strong ◯ c. stupid ◯ d. bold

6. In the selection, the word *reasoned* (line 6) means _____.

◯ a. wondered ◯ b. seasoned ◯ c. thought ◯ d. because

Analyzing Plot, Setting, and Character

Tests about stories also ask you about the characters, setting, and plot.

Here is a sample passage. Read the selection and the question that follows.

As I went along, I could not help but think back on the happy days with Father and Mother in Nanam, Korea. We lived in a beautiful big house with many different-sized tatami-mat rooms. Our home was surrounded by a graceful bamboo grove. My stomach was always filled with good food. I had plenty of clothes to wear and several pairs of fine shoes.

However, just before midnight on July 29, 1945, Mother, Ko, and I had to flee. We had learned from a friend in the Japanese army, Corporal Matsumura, that the Communists were about to attack our town. Father was away in Manchuria, and Hideyo was working in an ammunition factory twenty miles from home. We left Father and Hideyo a note asking them to meet us at the train station in Seoul. While we were fleeing to safety in the south, an airplane dropped a bomb and I was thrown into the air. This incident left me deaf in my right ear, and also with constant back pain. Until we reached Seoul, we lived on leaves from bushes and what Ko found on Korean farm-land. When we arrived in Seoul, we learned that atom bombs had been dropped on Nagasaki and Hiroshima, and that Japan had lost World War II. The Korean peninsula was divided in half and the Communists had taken over the north. We could never go back to our home in the bamboo grove. We had become refugees.

Who is the main character?
- ◯ a. Mother
- ◯ b. the narrator
- ◯ c. Father
- ◯ d. Hideyo

The correct answer is *b. the narrator.* The person who is telling the story is the main character, or most important person, in the selection.

Try It Yourself

Answer the following questions about the same passage. Fill in the oval next to the correct answer choice.

7. Where is the beginning of the story set?
- a. Manchuria
- b. Japan
- c. Nanam, Korea
- d. Hiroshima

8. How did the narrator become deaf in one ear?
- a. from the Japanese army
- b. from a bomb dropped by an airplane
- c. from eating leaves from bushes
- d. from being dropped as a baby

9. Why couldn't the family return home?
- a. The Communists had taken over the north.
- b. They could not find Father and Hideyo.
- c. They forgot their keys.
- d. Corporal Matsumura stopped them.

10. Where is the end of the story set?
- a. Hiroshima
- b. Seoul, Korea
- c. Manchuria
- d. Nagasaki

11. What happens to the characters in the story?
- a. They join the army.
- b. They become rich and famous.
- c. They find Hideyo.
- d. They become refugees.

Short-Answer Items

Short-answer items can be handled in a few words. It is not necessary to answer in complete sentences unless the directions say otherwise. Here is a sample.

Read the passage. Then write the response to each item in the space provided.

> *The following afternoon Miguel took the helm and steered the* ponga *homeward. As the boat skimmed past the rock reef, Tomás stood on the bow and looked down into the red-orange sea, which now reflected the colors of the sunset. He saw nothing larger than the parrot fish.*
>
> *The* ponga *shot out of the cove and into the Shallows, which lay between the island and the peninsula. The water was only about fifteen feet deep. Many sharks came here to give birth to their live young or to lay eggs, as some do. Into these protected waters also came old and ill sharks. They could slow their continuous swimming by heading into the currents and letting the swiftly flowing water rush through their gills. They used less energy this way and could rest and heal themselves. And into these waters came the Torres men to maintain their reputation as Loreto's best shark fishermen. The Shallows were sometimes called the Torres.*
>
> •What is the *ponga*?_____

To answer this question, look back to the first time the word *ponga* appears. The first sentence of the selection says that Miguel took the helm of the *ponga*. *Helm* is the word for the steering place in a boat. So a *ponga* must be a boat. Reading the next sentence shows that this is correct. You would write "a boat" in the space provided.

This question asks you to define a word used in the passage. That's one way to test how well you understand what you have read. Other questions may ask you to find facts in the passage, or to draw conclusions based on facts in the passage. Still others may ask you about setting, plot, or character.

Whenever you are asked to read a passage and answer questions about it, you should first read the whole passage to get a general understanding of what it is about. Then read each question, and scan through the passage again looking for the specific facts you need.

Try It Yourself

Reread the passage on page 24. Then complete the items.

12. Where is the Shallows? _____

_____

13. What characters appear in this selection?

_____

14. For what two main reasons did old and ill sharks go into the Shallows?

_____

_____

_____

15. About how deep is the water in the Shallows?

_____

16. For what other reason did sharks come to the Shallows?

_____

17. Why did the Torres men go into these waters?

_____

18. What other name did people give to the Shallows?

_____

19. Why do you think they called it that?

_____

_____

Long-Answer Items

Some reading tests may ask for answers in the form of complete sentences or paragraphs. It is important to support your responses by using your own conclusions as well as facts from the selection.

Here is a sample of this kind of item. Read the passage and the item that follows.

One day Babette Frühauf found a little girl amidst the ruins of a house. The child was weeping bitterly.

"Oh, my god, whatever are you doing here?" muttered the old newspaperwoman.

The girl did not reply. She crouched in front of the remains of a wall upon which Victory Is Ours had been painted in large white letters. Beneath this, an arrow pointed to the letters A and S, which stood for Air-raid Shelter. At some earlier time, there must have been a cellar window where the arrow pointed. Now there was nothing but a hole scarcely large enough for a dog to crawl through. "Oh, my dear god!" said the old woman.

The little girl squatted there, weeping. The old newspaper lady bent down low near the hole and cried, "Hello! Hello! Is anybody else still there?" Nothing moved. She stroked the girl and tried to console her, but the child would not be calmed. Tears washed narrow courses in the layer of dust on her cheeks.

"There, there, it will be all right," old Babette Frühauf murmured. Her voice trembled a little. She put her arm around the girl and pressed the child's head against her shoulder. "Now tell me what your name is."

A rather long time went by with no answer.

"Tell me now, it's important," she urged until the child finally whispered "Rebecca."

•What is the setting of this selection? Explain your reasons for your response.

Long-answer questions give you space to explain your answers fully. Here is a possible response:

> The selection does not tell exactly where or when the story takes place. It is set in the ruins of a house, near a small hole that was probably the entrance to an Air-Raid Shelter. It seems as if there is a war going on. You can also guess from Babette Frühauf's German name that the story takes place in Germany.

This is a good response to the question. For her answer, the writer uses facts and inferences from the story, as well as her own knowledge and ideas.

Try It Yourself

Now answer these questions about the same passage.

20. What kind of woman is Babette Frühauf?

_____

_____

_____

_____

_____

_____

21. Why do you think Rebecca is crying?

_____

_____

_____

_____

_____

READING NONFICTION

Some tests check your reading skills with nonfiction passages. They may ask you questions about the facts in these selections. They may also ask questions about information that the selection only hints at. Sometimes you will be asked to draw your own conclusions about the passage. The formats of these tests can be multiple-choice, short-answer, or long-answer.

Reading for Facts

Facts are statements that can be proven true. Reading tests often ask you multiple-choice questions about the facts in a nonfiction selection. Even if the selection is long, relax. Here are some hints that will get you through.

Here's an example. Read this nonfiction selection, then complete the items below. Fill in the oval next to the correct choice. If the correct response is not given, mark NG.

> *Fish need oxygen to live, just as land animals do. They have gills instead of lungs to get oxygen underwater.*
>
> *To breathe, a fish opens its mouth and draws in water. The water has oxygen. It flows over the gills, which are behind the mouth. The gills absorb the oxygen from the water and release waste gases into the water. This waste water goes back into the ocean through openings on the sides of the fish's head. These openings are covered by movable flaps.*
>
> •A fish's gills absorb ____.
>
> ○ a. lungs   ○ c. oxygen
> ○ b. waste gases   ○ d. NG

To find the correct response, scan the passage. Lines 1-2 say, "They have gills instead of lungs to get oxygen…" And line 4 reads, "The gills absorb the oxygen from the water. . ." So the correct response is *c. oxygen*.

Try It Yourself

22. Waste water gets back into the ocean through _____.
    a. openings on the fish's head
    b. the fish's mouth
    c. a narrow tube
    d. NG

Read the selection below and choose the best response for each item. If the correct response is not given, mark NG.

A jet took off in a January snowstorm from Washington, DC. Only minutes later, it crashed into the Potomac River. Passengers bobbing in the freezing water needed help, and they needed it fast.

Helicopter pilot Don Usher flew over the water until he saw someone. He brought his chopper as close to the woman and the water as he could. Then he tossed her a lifeline and pulled her to shore. As soon as she was safe, he flew over the water again to rescue someone else.

23. How did the passengers get into the Potomac River?
    ○ a. Their jet crashed.
    ○ b. They were swimming.
    ○ c. Their boat turned over.
    ○ d. NG

24. What helped Don Usher rescue the woman?
    ○ a. a dog   ○ c. a lifeline
    ○ b. warm clothes   ○ d. NG

Making Inferences

Sometimes a reading test will have an item for which the response is not directly stated in the selection. When a response is not clearly stated (as facts are), you often have to read between the lines to find it. The process is not very different from using clues to solve a mystery. This is called **making inferences.** Often you will be asked to write your responses to such items in short-answer form.

Here is a sample. Read the selection and complete the item that follows.

On November 22, 1935, crowds rushed to San Francisco Bay. People stood on tiptoe, jumped up on their cars, and scrambled onto rooftops for a better look. Overhead, fireworks rained down on the harbor where boats sounded their horns. A company of Boy Scouts unfurled the American flag. The air was charged with excitement.

At the center of this celebration, the main attraction floated calmly on the water. It was a huge airplane known as the China Clipper.

• Why were people in San Francisco so excited on November 22, 1935?

_____

The story selection does not directly state why people in San Francisco were excited that day. But from the information that is given, you can make the inference that it is because of the huge airplane floating in San Francisco Bay. You can also infer that there is something special about the airplane. So you might respond with the following: *Because of the huge, unusual airplane floating in the bay.*

Try It Yourself

Read the selection and answer the questions.

[Dorothy Molter grew up in Chicago but spent 56 years on a wilderness island. She was the last resident of the Boundary Waters Canoe Area Wilderness (Minnesota).]

Through the years Dorothy helped many campers. Because she was a nurse, she could aid anyone who was sick or injured. She sold food at cost to campers who ran out. Later she made her own root beer and gave it to visitors for a donation. By doing this, Dorothy earned the name the Root Beer Lady, and many campers went out of their way to stop and see her.

Dorothy liked life in the wilderness and had no desire to leave it. She died on her island, of natural causes, at age 79 in December 1986. In order to restore the land to its natural condition, her log cabin, tent, and personal belongings were moved to Ely and set up as a museum.

25. How old was Dorothy when she moved to the island?

_____

26. Was Dorothy lonely on the island? Why or why not?

_____

_____

_____

27. Why did she remain on the island for such a long time?

_____

_____

28. What happened to Dorothy's belongings after she died?

_____

_____

Drawing Conclusions

Reading tests may also use nonfiction selections to check your ability to draw conclusions. When you are asked to draw conclusions, you can't use only what is stated in the selection. You must also use your own knowledge and experience to create your response. Often these questions will ask you for a long response—several sentences, a paragraph, or even an essay.

Here is an example. Read this selection and then look at the question below.

Hints:

- When you are asked to draw conclusions, make sure you are not just restating facts from the selection. Your conclusions should give your own point of view.
- There may be more than one correct response to this type of item. But answers that are not based on the facts of the selection will be wrong.

The China Clipper *was no ordinary airplane. To begin with, it was a seaplane—a plane that landed and took off from water. This flying boat, as it was called, had a watertight body that let it float just like a ship.*

The Clipper *was also enormous. From its rounded nose to its upswept tail fins, it measured 91 feet. Its height, from the base of its curved hull to the top of its wing, was 25 feet. From tip to tip, the wings spanned 130 feet. The* China Clipper *was the biggest and most beautifully built airplane the world had yet seen. . . .*

Amid the hubbub, the engines roared to life and warmed up for takeoff. Hundreds of newsreel cameras focused on the plane. Reporters swarmed the docks. Around the world, millions of people tuned in their radios to hear history in the making.

This fantastic event was a shining moment in the dark depths of the Great Depression. For a short time, people could forget about such problems as hunger and unemployment. Perhaps for a moment the China Clipper *could help even the poorest folks believe in magic.*

- Write a paragraph to answer the following: Why did the *China Clipper* get so much attention when first launched?

This question asks you to draw a conclusion from information in the selection. To do it, you would need to:

- Scan the selection for the information you need.
- Put it together with your own ideas.
- Make some notes.
- Write your answer in paragraph form.

(Continue to page 32)

Here is a good response to the question from page 31:

The <u>China Clipper</u> got a lot of attention when it was launched for several reasons. First, it could take off and land on water. Second, it was bigger and better built than any plane before it. And finally, it was launched during the Great Depression, a time when people needed to hear some good news for a change.

The writer uses facts from the passage and his own ideas. He draws the conclusion that the *China Clipper* got attention for several reasons. Then he supports it by listing the reasons. He saves the most important one for last. The paragraph is organized with a topic sentence and three related supporting sentences. Finally, it uses complete sentences and correct spelling and punctuation.

Try It Yourself

29. On the lines below, write a paragraph to answer the following: What title would you give the selection you just read? Why do you think this is the best title for the selection?

_____

_____

_____

_____

_____

30. Think of a recent event that caused a lot of excitement. On the lines below, write about why that event was so exciting. You may want to compare it with what you read about the launching of the *China Clipper*.

_____

_____

_____

_____

_____

TESTS ABOUT WRITING

Most writing tests will give you a certain type of writing to do. For example, you may be asked to write a personal narrative, a business letter, a problem/solution paper, or even a process (how-to) paper. This section will give you help with some of the most important of these types of writing.

But first, here are some reminders about what a test-grader will look for when reading *any* type of writing test.

A test-grader will check that you have:

- done the type of writing the test asks for

- organized your ideas so they make sense to a reader

- used complete sentences

- used correct punctuation and capitalization

- used words correctly and spelled them right

Checking Capitalization

You probably won't be tested separately on spelling, capitalization, and punctuation in a writing test. But a test-grader will look at these things when grading your test. Some review will help you do your best.

Checking Punctuation

Just as each sentence must begin with a capital letter, it must end with an end mark. Different types of sentences use different end marks. Make sure that you are using them correctly.

Remember

Always capitalize:

- the first word in any sentence
- the names of persons
- the pronoun I
- the names of towns and cities, states, countries, and planets (New York State, Salt Lake City)
- particular places, things, or events (Rose Bowl, Lincoln Memorial)
- historical events and periods, and special events (Ice Age, World Series, Martin Luther King Day)
- the full names of groups or organizations (National Aeronautics and Space Administration)
- the days of the week, the names of months, and holidays

Remember

- A period ends a sentence that describes or tells something.
- A question mark ends a sentence that asks a question.
- An exclamation point ends a sentence that shows excitement or strong feeling. Sometimes a sentence can be punctuated with either a period or an exclamation point, depending on the emotion the writer wants to express.

Checking Spelling

When checking your spelling on a writing test, remember the basic spelling rules you have learned over the years, along with the following hints. If you find you have misspelled a word, neatly erase or cross it out and write it correctly.

Here are a few spelling rules to remember:

- Adding a prefix to a word does not usually change the spelling of the original word. (*im* + *mortal* = *immortal*)
- Adding suffixes like *-ness* and *-ly* does not usually change the spelling of the original word unless the word ends in *y*. Then the *y* is often changed to *i*. (*usual* + *ly* = *usually*; *weary* + *ness* = *weariness*)
- If a word ends in *e* and a suffix begins with a vowel, drop the *e* before adding the suffix. (*expire* + *ation* = *expiration*)
- Don't forget spelling rules like *i* before *e* except after *c*.

Remember

Homophones are words that sound alike but are spelled differently, such as *write* and *right*. Make sure you have chosen the right spelling.

Writing Complete Sentences

On writing tests, test-graders also check for complete sentences. A complete sentence needs a subject and a predicate.

Here is some help for checking your own sentences.

SUBJECT PART	PREDICATE PART
The class	went on a trip.

Try It Yourself

Read each sentence. Then underline the subject part. The first one is done for you.

- Before breakfast, <u>Captain Hernandez</u> goes for a swim.

Captain Hernandez is the one who is doing the action in the sentence.

31. Swimming strengthens most of the body's muscles.

32. When you run, your heart beats faster.

33. A marathon race covers 26 miles 385 yards.

Read each sentence. Then underline the predicate part. The first one is done for you.

- A strange creature <u>emerged from the depths</u>.

Emerged from the depths tells what the subject (*a strange creature*) did.

34. Many kinds of bears get angry quite quickly.

35. Alligators live 50 to 60 years.

36. No two giraffes have their spots in the same pattern.

Remember

- A sentence must express a complete thought.
- The subject part is the part of the sentence that contains a noun or pronoun and tells who or what does something.
- The predicate part is the part of the sentence that contains a verb and says something about the subject.
- Sentences need correct capitalization and punctuation.

34

Avoiding Fragments and Run-On Sentences

To do your best on writing tests, you will also need to know how to avoid fragments and run-on sentences.

Here is a sample item. Read it. Which choice (a., b., or c.) best describes the sample group of words? Fill in the oval.

- On the waters.

  ◯ a. complete sentence
  ◯ b. fragment
  ◯ c. run-on sentence

The correct answer is *b. fragment.* *On the waters* is not a complete thought.

Try It Yourself

Read each item. Then fill in the oval that correctly describes each group of words.

SUPER TEST-TAKER TIP:
PACE YOURSELF

What might happen if you put all your effort into the first part of a test? You might "run out of steam" for the second part. To do your best on a test, think of it as a long-distance race. Pace yourself so you will do as well on the last part as you did on the first part of the test.

---

37. When it came into sight.

◯ a. complete sentence
◯ b. fragment
◯ c. run-on sentence

38. It scared me I jumped.

◯ a. complete sentence
◯ b. fragment
◯ c. run-on sentence

39. The joke was on us.

◯ a. complete sentence
◯ b. fragment
◯ c. run-on sentence

40. No one knew where we were.

◯ a. complete sentence
◯ b. fragment
◯ c. run-on sentence

Writing Personal Narratives

On a writing test, you may be asked to write a personal narrative. For example, you may be asked to narrate, or describe, an important experience you have had. When writing a personal narrative, keep the following in mind:

- Tell what happened in chronological order—the order in which it happened.

- Remember that your reader was not there. Be sure to include everything your reader will need to understand your story.

- Do not just tell what happened. Also tell your feelings and reactions to the event or experience. You may also want to put in anything you learned or concluded from the experience.

- Make sure your piece of writing has a clear beginning, middle, and end.

- Make sure you stick to the topic.

Try It Yourself

Fear is something that everyone feels at some time. Tell about a time when you were afraid and describe what happened as a result.

Prewrite your first draft by completing each exercise. Write your answers on the lines provided.

Stage 1: Brainstorm

41. List five instances when you felt really, really scared. Talk about it with a partner. It'll help jar your memory.

1. _____
2. _____
3. _____
4. _____
5. _____

Stage 2: Pick a Topic

42. Choose one of the events you've already listed, then list five things about that event you plan to include in your narrative.

1. _____
2. _____
3. _____
4. _____
5. _____

Stage 3: First Draft

43. Now you are ready to write your first draft. Combine all the elements you have already listed and write a first draft on the lines below. (If you need more space, use a clean sheet of paper.)

When you are finished, reread what you have written. Mark the words or places that need to be revised, and proofread your draft for spelling and grammar. Then, write a second draft on another sheet of paper.

SUPER TEST-TAKER TIP: WRITING YOUR OPENING PARAGRAPH

In a personal narrative, or any piece of writing, make sure your introduction (opening paragraph) is dramatic and interesting. This way it will capture the reader's attention right away. If not, chances are the reader will read no further. A good introduction could be an interesting question; a joke; or a sentence that mentions an unusual, delightful, or scary event. The key is to grab your reader's attention.

Writing a Problem/Solution Paper

In a problem/solution paper, you will be asked to explain a problem and develop a solution for that problem. Here's what you need to remember when you are writing this type of paper.

- Explain the problem as clearly as possible.
- Explain the solution in a clear and convincing way.
- Make sure your reader understands why you believe your solution is the best one.

Proofreading Your Written Work

Always save time to read over your writing. This proofreading checklist can help you polish your work

Proofreading Checklist

❑ Have I used complete sentences?

❑ Will a reader understand what I have written?

❑ Have I checked the spelling of all words?

❑ Have I used capitalization correctly?

❑ Have I used the correct punctuation and end marks?

Try It Yourself

44. Use the lines below to make a list of some problems in your school or community that you feel can be easily resolved. For each problem write your solution. Then number your problems and solutions from the most interesting to the least.

_____

_____

_____

_____

_____

_____

_____

_____

Try It Yourself

45. On the lines below, build on the most interesting problem/solution you listed and write a paper.

_____

_____

_____

_____

_____

_____

_____

_____

_____

_____

_____

_____

_____

_____

_____

_____

_____

_____

_____

UNIT: 3 TESTS ABOUT MATH

Tests about math include many different types of problems. Some of them use number facts. Some give you geometric shapes to work with or ask you to do measuring. Other math tests will give you problems to solve or ask you math questions based on graphs or charts. By using what you will learn and practice in this unit, you will feel more confident about taking all of these types of math tests.

TESTS WITH NUMBER FACTS

When you take tests with numbers, one little mistake in computing can give you a wrong answer. So be careful when you compute. Follow these tips.

- Be sure numbers are lined up in the correct column.
- Round only the numbers the question asks you to. Also be sure you are rounding the correct numbers.
- Use opposite processes to check your work. Use addition to check subtraction and multiplication to check division—and vice versa.

Hint

- When you are taking tests with word problems, use scratch paper to work them out.
- Use mental math for simple addition, subtraction, multiplication, and division.
- Reduce all fractions.
- For some problems it may be easier to convert unlike items to like items before you calculate. (For instance, if dealing with inches and feet, convert one or the other so they are alike before calculating.)
- On multiple-choice tests, try to figure out the answer before you read the answer choices.

Here are some examples. A math test may ask you to solve the following item:

- 4 ft. ÷ 3 = _____

First convert feet to inches:
   4 ft. = 48 inches.

Then do the calculations:
   48 inches ÷ 3 = 16 inches.

Finally, reconvert:
   16 inches = 1 ft. 4 inches.

For other problems, you may not need to do the conversion first.

- 5 hrs. 23 mins. x 3 = _____

In this case it is easier to do the multiplication first, then convert:

5 hrs. x 3 = 15 hrs.

23 mins. x 3 = 69 mins.

Now convert:

69 mins. = 1 hr. 9 mins.

Finally, combine the parts:

15 hrs. + 1 hr. 9 mins. = 16 hrs. 9 mins.

Try It Yourself

Fill in the oval next to the correct answer. If the correct answer is not among the choices, mark NG.

SUPER TEST-TAKER TIP:
ESTIMATION

You can help catch errors if you estimate the answer before you work out a problem. If, after you work it out, the answer is very different from your estimate, then recheck your work. In a multiple-choice test, the answers that are not close to your estimate are probably incorrect.

---

1. 3 x 4 ft. 7 in. =
- a. 12 ft. 11 in.
- b. 12 ft. 10 in.
- c. 13 ft. 9 in.
- d. NG

2. 8 km 400 m + 700 m =
- a. 8 km 900 m
- b. 8 km 1200 m
- c. 9 km 100 m
- d. NG

3. 6 x 740 m =
- a. 42 km 240 m
- b. 4 km 200 m
- c. 4 km 420 m
- d. NG

4. 48 min. + 59 min. =
- a. 1 hr. 7 min.
- b. 1 hr. 17 min.
- c. 1 hr. 47 min.
- d. NG

5. Which is the correct order of these fractions from small to large?

$$\frac{1}{4} \quad \frac{1}{2} \quad \frac{1}{8} \quad \frac{1}{6} \quad \frac{1}{3}$$

- a. $\frac{1}{2} \ \frac{1}{3} \ \frac{1}{4} \ \frac{1}{6} \ \frac{1}{8}$
- b. $\frac{1}{8} \ \frac{1}{6} \ \frac{1}{4} \ \frac{1}{3} \ \frac{1}{2}$
- c. $\frac{1}{6} \ \frac{1}{8} \ \frac{1}{2} \ \frac{1}{3} \ \frac{1}{4}$
- d. NG

6. 2 weeks 5 days + 33 days =
- a. 6 weeks 9 days
- b. 7 weeks 3 days
- c. 6 weeks 5 days
- d. NG

7. 9 yards x 42 feet =
- a. 126 sq. yds
- b. 108 sq. yds
- c. 378 sq. yds
- d. NG

(Continue to page 42)

8. Which of these numbers is $4329.86 rounded to the nearest ten?

○ a. $4330   ○ c. $4000

○ b. $4320   ○ d. $3200

9. Which of these numbers is 350 when rounded to the nearest ten and 300 when rounded to the nearest hundred?

○ a. 336   ○ c. 352

○ b. 346   ○ d. 359

10. Which letter best represents $4\frac{5}{6}$?

○ a. M   ○ c. O

○ b. N   ○ d. P

11. Which one is the numeric form of three hundred thousand nine hundred forty-seven?

○ a. 3,947   ○ c. 300,947

○ b. 394,700   ○ d. 30,947

12. In writing, explain how you would solve the problem.

4 ft. 7 in. – 3 ft. 11 in.

_____

_____

_____

_____

TESTS WITH PROBLEMS TO SOLVE

Tests with problems to solve have their own special difficulties. One of the most challenging is time.

Almost all tests have a time limit. You need to finish all or as much of the test as you can within the set time. Even if you don't get any answers wrong, your score will be low if you only finish a few test items. So on math tests with problems to solve, you may want to skip difficult items and return to them later. This way, you'll complete as many problems as you can in the time allowed.

Be sure to:

- Finish as many items as you can.
- Make a small mark next to the items you skip.
- When you skip an item, be sure you skip the answer space as well. Keep your place in the rows of answer spaces.
- If you finish the easier items before time is up, go back to the more difficult ones.

Working with Word Problems

Here are some special tips to follow for word problems.

- When you are taking math tests with word problems, read each problem carefully. Then make sure you know what you are asked to find and what number facts to use.
- If you are really stuck, sketch out the problem with pictures.
- Estimate the answer.
- Work out the problem in your mind, or write out the problem as an equation.
- Use scratch paper to work out the problem, or use your calculator if allowed.

- Check the answer against your estimate.
- On multiple-choice tests, work out your own answer before you read the answer choices.
- Write out the answer for short-answer questions.

Choosing the Operation

To solve a problem, you must decide which operation, or mathematical procedure, to use.

Start by looking carefully at the problem. Do you need to add, subtract, multiply, or divide? As you read, look for key words that will alert you to the operation: *how many, are left, in all, for each,* and so on.

For some math-test questions, you may need to use more than one operation to solve the problem. If so, figure out which operation comes first, which comes second, and so on. Here are some examples.

- Deirdre baked 72 cookies for her 8 guests. How many cookies will each guest get?

  ◯a. 64   ◯b. 576   ◯c. 9   ◯d. NG

In this item, the word *each* tells you that it is a division problem. To get the correct answer you would divide 72 by 8. The answer is *c. 9.*

- Denzel is 23 years old. His sister Ebony is 15 years younger than he is. How old is Ebony?

  ◯a. 8   ◯b. 38   ◯c. 18   ◯d. NG

The key word in this problem is *younger.* Since Ebony is 15 years younger than Denzel, you have to subtract 15 from 23 in order to figure out her age, which is *a. 8.*

Sometimes, in order to answer math questions with two or more stages, you need to choose the right operation for each stage.

- Carla has 12 part-time employees. Four of them make $5.00 an hour, and eight of them make $6.00 an hour. If every one works 20 hours a week, how much does Carla pay altogether in weekly wages?

The first process in this problem is multiplication. You can use multiplication to figure out how much money each person in each group of employees earns for a 20-hour work week.

$5.00 per hour x 20 hours = $100

Each person in the group that makes $5.00 an hour earns $100 per week.

$6.00 per hour x 20 hours = $120

Each person in the group that makes $6.00 an hour earns $120 per week.

Next, figure out how much each group of employees makes. This calls for multiplication again.

$100 x 4 employees = $400 for the $5.00 an hour group

$120 x 8 employees = $960 for the $6.00 an hour group

Now, look at the problem again. The word *altogether* suggests a final step that requires addition. The weekly wages of both groups must now be added in order to figure out how much Carla pays both groups (altogether).

$400 + $960 = $1360

The correct answer is $1360.

Try It Yourself

Fill in the oval next to the correct answer choice. Show your work in the space to the right.

Use the following information for items 13-16. Kristy's mother baked an apple pie. She gave Kristy $\frac{2}{8}$, Michael $\frac{1}{4}$, and Rhonda $\frac{3}{8}$.

13. How much of the pie is left?

- a. $\frac{1}{2}$ c. $\frac{1}{4}$
- b. $\frac{1}{8}$ d. $\frac{2}{8}$

14. Which two people received the same amount of pie?

- a. Kristy and Michael
- b. Michael and Rhonda
- c. Rhonda and Kristy
- d. none of them

15. Which is the biggest piece of pie?

- a. Kristy's   c. Rhonda's
- b. Michael's   d. the piece left over

16. If Michael gave Rhonda half of his pie, how much pie would she have in all?

- a. $\frac{1}{6}$ c. $\frac{5}{8}$
- b. $\frac{3}{8}$ d. $\frac{1}{2}$

44

Try It Yourself

For items 17-22 use the price chart for Dino's Market.

Work out your answers in the blank areas, then write them in the spaces.

Dino's Market

Vegetables

Broccoli . . . . .99¢ per bunch
Potatoes . . . .$1.29 per lb.
Carrots . . . . .99¢ per bag of 8
Onions . . . .$1.29 per lb.
Peppers (green) . . . . .99¢ per lb.

Fruit

Bananas . . . . .69¢ per lb.
Oranges . . . . .8/$1.04
Grapefruit . . . . .4/$1.20
Apples . . . . .49¢ per lb.
Limes . . . . .6/$1.20
Kiwi . . . . .4/$1.00
Melons $1.19

17. What is the least expensive item per pound at Dino's Market?_____

18. How much would 5 pounds of potatoes cost?

_____

19. How much would 40 oranges cost? Explain how you would find out.

_____

_____

_____

20. Ahmed paid $5.40 for limes. How many did he buy?

_____

21. How much would 4 pounds of bananas, 2 melons, 6 grapefruit, and 12 kiwi fruit cost?_____

22. How much would the same merchandise cost with a 10% discount? _____

Fill in the oval next to the correct response. If the correct response is not among the choices, mark NG. For item 27 write your response in the space provided.

23. There are 802 students at Joanne's school. On Friday, 46 were absent. How many attended school?

○ a. 766   ○ c. 776
○ b. 756   ○ d. NG

24. Yvette paid taxi fares of $4.50, $6.80, $10.00, and $3.50. What was her average fare?

○ a. $24.80   ○ c. $6.20
○ b. $4.76   ○ d. NG

25. Darryl's family wants to buy a computer. The computer with 4K of memory costs $2,369.99. The computer with 6K of memory costs $3,988.99. How much will Darryl's family save if they buy the computer with 4K of memory?

○ a. $1619.00   ○ c. $6359.99
○ b. $1719.99   ○ d. NG

26. Umberto worked 23 hours and made $103.50. Which number sentence would you use to find out how much money Umberto makes per hour?

○ a. $103.50 x 23
○ b. $103.50 − 23
○ c. $103.50 ÷ 23
○ d. NG

27. Fern's basketball team scored 15 points in the first quarter, 22 points in the second quarter, 18 points in the third quarter, and 33 points in the fourth quarter. What was the average number of points they scored in each quarter? Explain the correct way to solve this problem.

_____

_____

_____

_____

_____

_____

_____

_____

_____

_____

SHAPING UP

In some math tests, you need to solve problems that involve geometric shapes. To solve these problems, use what you already know about geometric shapes and their properties.

Here are a few tips to remember about geometry items.

- A triangle has three sides and three angles. The sum of the angles is 180°.
- An acute triangle has three acute angles. That means each angle measures less than 90°.
- A right triangle has one right angle that measures 90°.
- An obtuse triangle has one obtuse angle that measures between 90° and 180°.
- A parallelogram is a figure in which the opposite sides are parallel.

You have also learned about other geometric figures and properties that are not listed here. Make sure you review this information. You will need to know it for most math tests.

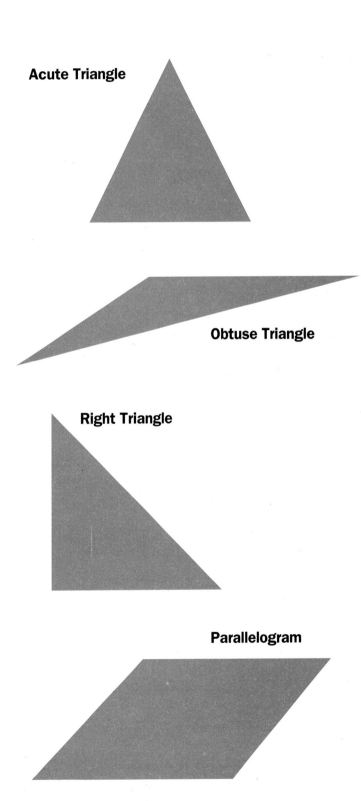

Acute Triangle

Obtuse Triangle

Right Triangle

Parallelogram

Try It Yourself

Fill in the oval next to the correct response.
If the correct response is not among the
choices, mark NG.

Use the following figures for items 28 and 29.

a.　　　　　　　　　b.　　　　　c.

28. Which figure is not a rectangle?
○ a.　　　　○ b.　　　　○ c.　　　　○ d. NG

29. Which figure is not a parallelogram?
○ a.　　　　○ b.　　　　○ c.　　　　○ d. NG

30. Which figure below contains a right angle?
○ a.　　　　○ b.　　　　○ c.　　　　○ d. NG

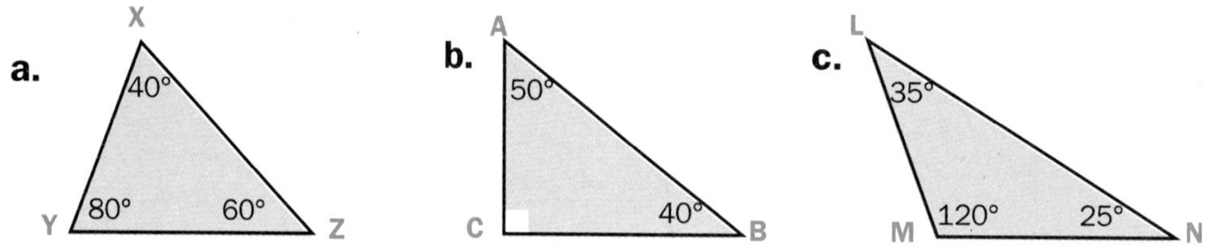

a.
X
40°
Y 80°   60° Z

b.
A
50°
C   40° B

c.
L
35°
M 120°   25° N

31. In the triangles above, which is an obtuse angle?
○ a. ABC　　○ b. XYZ　　○ c. LMN　　○ d. NG

32. In the figures below, which of the shaded regions does not represent $\frac{2}{3}$ of the figure?
○ a.　　　　○ b.　　　　○ c.　　　　○ d.

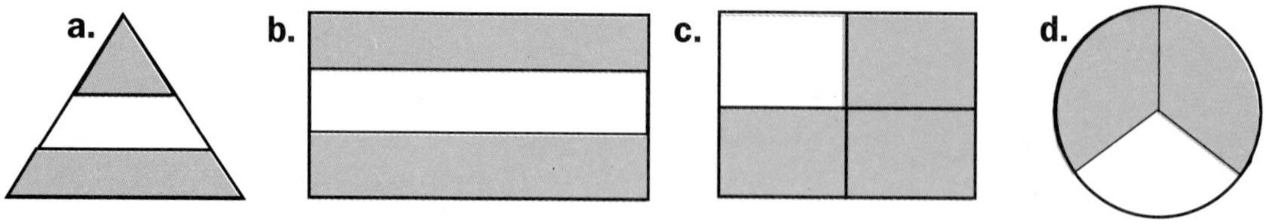

a.　　　　b.　　　　c.　　　　d.

33. Which two of the figures below represent the same fractional amount?
○ a. 1 and 3　　○ b. 2 and 4　　○ c. 1 and 2　　○ d. 3 and 4

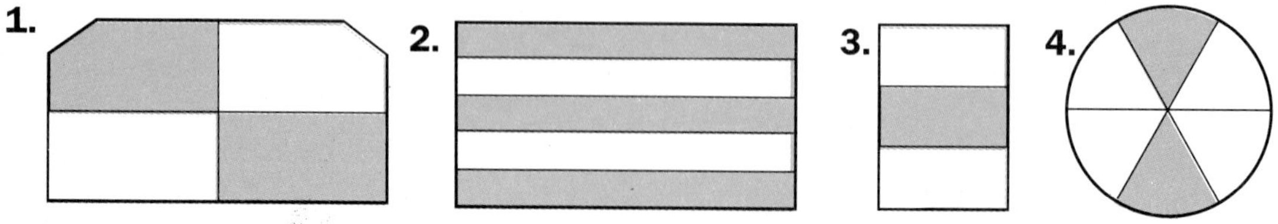

1.　　　　2.　　　　3.　　　　4.

MEASURE IT

Some math problems ask you to find different kinds of measurements. Review the different kinds of measurements and conversions you have already learned. Some of them are listed in the table.

In order to solve measurement problems, remember to follow these steps:

- Read carefully. Check for whether you need to convert from one measurement to another.
- Look back over the problem for only the facts that will help you solve the problem. Disregard the rest.
- Decide which operation the problem calls for.
- Work it out on scratch paper, or use a calculator if it is allowed.
- For multiple-choice questions, use mental math, estimate, and see if your answer matches any of the answer choices.

Common Measurements and Conversions	
1 foot	= 12 inches
1 yard	= 3 feet
1 tablespoon	= 3 teaspoons
1 cup	= 16 tablespoons
1 pint	= 2 cups
1 quart	= 2 pints
1 gallon	= 4 quarts
1 pint	= 16 fluid ounces
1 kilogram	= 1,000 grams
1 kilometer	= 1,000 meters
1 meter	= 39.37 inches
1 centimeter	= .01 meter

Try It Yourself

Solve the problems to answer questions 34-47. Fill in the oval next to the correct answer. If the correct answer is not among the choices, mark NG. Show your work in the spaces to the sides.

34. Sara wants to trim her handkerchief with lace. Each side of her handkerchief is seven inches. How many inches of lace does she need?

○ a. 14 ○ b. 17 ○ c. 56 ○ d. NG

(Continue to page 50)

49

35. Josh needs stakes for six small plants. He has a stick five feet long. If he cuts it into six equal pieces, how long will each piece be?

○ a. 8 in. ○ b. 10 in. ○ c. 11 in. ○ d. NG

36. The Corellis plan to line both sides of their driveway with colored tiles. If each tile is six inches square, how many tiles will they need to line their 36-foot driveway?

○ a. 36 ○ b. 72 ○ c. 144 ○ d. NG

37. Mrs. Lawson wants to put vinyl floor covering in her kitchen. The kitchen is 24 feet by 18 feet. How many square yards of floor covering does she need?

○ a. 48 ○ b. 8 ○ c. 6 ○ d. NG

38. Ivy has a piece of plywood 20 feet long. For an experiment, she needs eight pieces of equal length. How long will each piece be?

○ a. 12 in. ○ b. 18 in. ○ c. 35 in. ○ d. NG

39. Marco wants to put a fence around each of his five flower beds. Each one measures 6 feet by 15 feet. How many yards of fencing will Marco need altogether?

○ a. 30 ○ b. 90 ○ c. 70 ○ d. NG

40. Noah is 72 inches tall. If he wanted a doorway that was $1\frac{1}{2}$ times his height, how many feet would it be?

○ a. 7 ○ b. 9 ○ c. 21 ○ d. NG

41. To make tropical punch, Robin used one pint of orange juice, one cup of mango juice, $\frac{1}{2}$ cup of peach juice, and $\frac{1}{2}$ cup of lemon juice. How many quarts of punch did Robin make?

○ a. 1 ○ b. 2 ○ c. 3 ○ d. NG

42. Find the volume of this figure.

6in.　10 in.　2 in.

○ a. 12 cu. in.　　○ c. 18 cu. in.
○ b. 60 cu. in.　　○ d. NG

43. The Morenos want new carpeting for their living room. The room is 15 feet by 21 feet. Carpet costs $10 per square yard. How much will it cost them to carpet the room?
○ a. $250　　○ c. $450
○ b. $350　　○ d. NG

44. Manny has 5 pints of milk that he must pour into a 64-ounce container. How many pints will not fit?
○ a. 1　　○ c. 3
○ b. 2　　○ d. NG

45. Tina has nine breakfast customers in her diner. Two thirds of them want a regular-sized 8-ounce glass of juice, and the other third want the giant 16-ounce size. How many ounces of juice does she need?
○ a. 36　　○ c. 96
○ b. 71　　○ d. NG

46. The Grinkovs' ice cream shop sold 12 gallons of ice cream to their first 24 customers. If each of those customers purchased the same amount of ice cream, how many quarts did each one purchase?
○ a. 1　　○ c. 3
○ b. 2　　○ d. NG

47. Kyung served 50 quarts of juice at his birthday party. Each person received two cups of juice. Explain how you would find out how many people were at his party.

_____

_____

_____

TESTS WITH GRAPHS AND CHARTS

Some math tests ask questions about graphs and charts. You may even be asked to draw one yourself. Here are some ways you can prepare yourself to do your best on these types of math questions.

Pictures of Information

Graphs are pictures of information. Most graphs help you read information about numbers and amounts faster and more easily than you could in a paragraph. The different types of graphs—line graphs, bar graphs, circle graphs (also known as pie graphs), and so on—show information in different ways.

Line graphs often show how numbers or amounts change over time. An example might be the population of your state in 1960, 1970, 1980, and 1990.

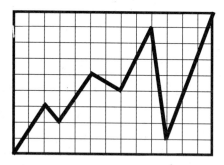

However, if you wanted to compare the 1990 populations of Los Angeles, New York, Miami, and Seattle, a **bar graph** would be better. Bar graphs often show comparisons between two or more items.

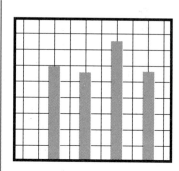

If you wanted to show in percentages how the money is spent in your state budget, you could use a **circle** or **pie graph.** Circle graphs use percents to show how the parts of something relate to a whole. Each section of a circle graph is a percentage of the whole graph, and the sum of the percents (sections) equals 100 percent.

A **chart** can provide easy-to-understand information as well. Charts are diagrams, maps, drawings, or tables that provide information about everything from budgets to weather to geography.

Here is an example of a test item involving a graph. Some tests might ask you to answer questions using a graph like the one below. This bar graph shows the number of book pages Jonathan and Kit read over a six-week period.

Hints:

- Read the graph or chart first.
- Next read the question.
- Look at the graph or chart again to find the answer to the question.

Book Pages Read in a Six-Week Period by Two Fifth-Graders

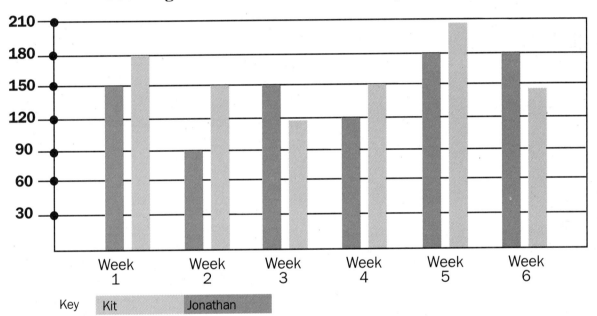

Key   Kit   Jonathan

• During which week were the most pages read by both children?

The correct answer is week 5. This is the only week in which both children read the greatest number of pages.

(Jonathan read the same number of pages in week 6 as he did in week 5, but Kit read fewer pages in that week.)

• In week 4, how many more pages did Kit read than Jonathan?

The correct answer is 30. In week 4, Kit's bar (the lighter one) goes up to 150. Jonathan's bar goes up to 120. When you subtract the number of pages Jonathan read from the number of pages Kit read, the difference is 30.

Try It Yourself

Now do these on your own. The students of Harding Junior High are planning a fair to raise money for the school. They created a circle graph to show how they planned to spend the profit. Use this budget to answer questions 48-51. Write the correct answer in the space provided.

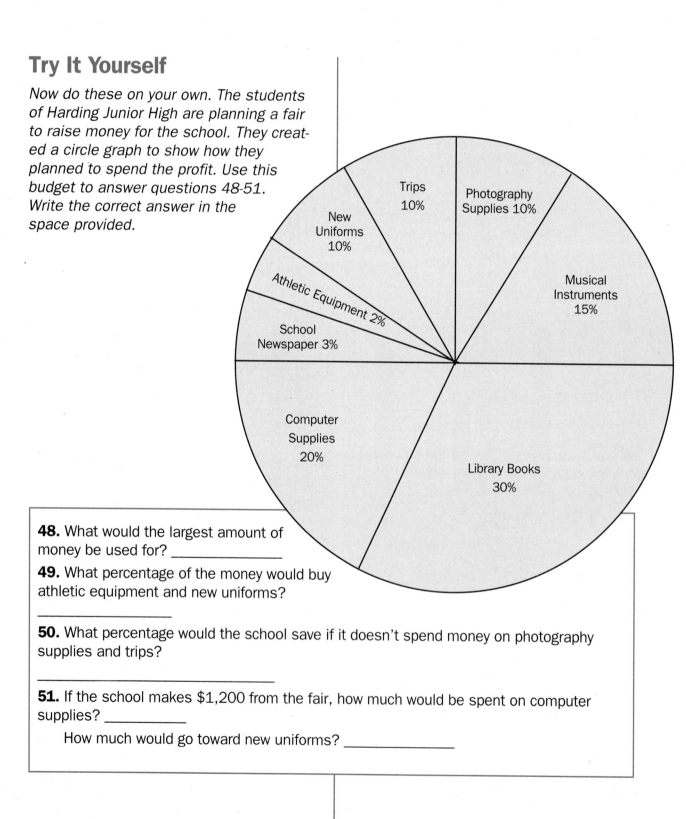

48. What would the largest amount of money be used for? _____

49. What percentage of the money would buy athletic equipment and new uniforms?

_____

50. What percentage would the school save if it doesn't spend money on photography supplies and trips?

_____

51. If the school makes $1,200 from the fair, how much would be spent on computer supplies? _____

How much would go toward new uniforms? _____

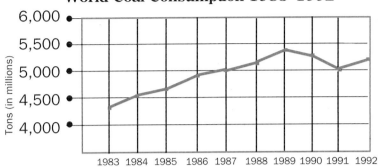

World Coal Consumption 1983–1992

Tons (in millions)

6,000
5,500
5,000
4,500
4,000

1983 1984 1985 1986 1987 1988 1989 1990 1991 1992

Use the line graph at right for items 52–55. Fill in the oval next to the correct answer.

52. How many million tons of coal were used in 1984?
- ○ a. 4,400
- ○ b. 4,500
- ○ c. 4,600
- ○ d. 4,700

53. During which year was coal usage the highest?
- ○ a. 1989
- ○ b. 1990
- ○ c. 1991
- ○ d. 1992

54. Coal usage was the same in all these years EXCEPT
- ○ a. 1987
- ○ b. 1988
- ○ c. 1991
- ○ d. 1992

55. Between which years did coal usage drop?
- ○ a. 1987 and 1991
- ○ b. 1988 and 1989
- ○ c. 1991 and 1992
- ○ d. 1990 and 1991

The line graph you used to answer the previous section's questions showed how world coal use changed over several years. The following bar graph compares the amount of coal several regions used in one year. Use this bar graph to respond to the next set of items. Fill in the oval next to the correct response.

World Coal Consumption (1992)

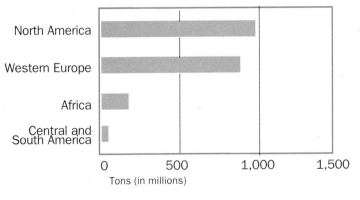

North America
Western Europe
Africa
Central and South America

0   500   1,000   1,500
Tons (in millions)

56. About how many million tons of coal were used in Western Europe in 1992?
- ○ a. 400
- ○ b. 500
- ○ c. 800
- ○ d. 1,000

57. In which region was coal usage highest?
- ○ a. North America
- ○ b. Western Europe
- ○ c. Africa
- ○ d. Central and South America

58. In which region was coal usage lowest?
- ○ a. North America
- ○ b. Western Europe
- ○ c. Africa
- ○ d. Central and South America

59. Which region produced the largest amount of coal in 1992?
- ○ a. North America
- ○ b. Africa
- ○ c. Western Europe
- ○ d. can't tell from this graph

TESTS WITH PROJECTS TO DO

Some math tests use a project or written report to check your knowledge and skills. You may be asked to work with others to complete the project. If so, be sure to follow these steps:

- There is often more than one solution. Try to reach agreement. Otherwise, be prepared to compromise or go along with the decision of the majority.
- Work cooperatively. Divide the work so that each group member knows exactly what to do. Do your best on your task and help others do their best, too.
- Be positive with other group members. Support them and tell them that you appreciate what they do.
- Work together on the final product.

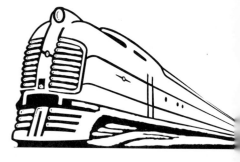

Try It Yourself

Work in a group of three and complete this project by fully answering each question. Use the list of information along with th charts. Make sure you read each part carefully. Use scratch pape to do the work, then write your responses on the lines provided.

Mr. and Mrs. Viola have a business meeting in Atlanta at 8:00 a.m. Tuesday. They must decide which mode of round-trip transportation best suits their time and budget. They must also keep the following in mind:

- They can't leave home until after 3:00 p.m. Monday.
- If they take a flight that leaves between 3:00 p.m. and 5:00 p.m., they can purchase one of the two tickets at half price.
- They want to get proper rest before the meeting.
- The hotel costs $39.99 per person for guests who register before 10:30 p.m. and $54.99 per person for guests arriving afterward.
- Trains that leave between 7:00 p.m. and midnight give a $\frac{1}{3}$ discount on each ticket.
- The Violas have a combined travel budget of $300 for transportation and hotel.

PLANES TO ATLANTA			
Departures	Day	Arrivals	Day
0:55 a.m.	M	1:55 p.m.	M
1:15 p.m.	M	7:35 p.m.	M
0:00 p.m.	M	1:25 a.m.	Tu

FARE: $125 per person/round-trip

TRAINS TO ATLANTA			
Departures	Day	Arrivals	Day
7:05 a.m.	M	1:35 p.m.	M
3:55 p.m.	M	11:00 p.m.	M
7:40 p.m.	M	2:10 a.m.	Tu

FARE: $111 per person/round-trip

BUSES TO ATLANTA			
Departures	Day	Arrivals	Day
10:10 a.m.	M	12:35 a.m.	Tu
3:25 p.m.	M	1:25 a.m.	Tu
5:00 p.m.	M	3:15 a.m.	Tu

FARE: $65 per person/round-trip
(Afternoon service is express.)

60. What choices could Mr. and Mrs. Viola eliminate? Why?

_____
_____
_____
_____
_____
_____
_____
_____
_____
_____
_____
_____
_____
_____

61. What choice is best for them? Why?

_____
_____
_____
_____
_____
_____
_____
_____
_____
_____
_____
_____
_____

62. Work with one other classmate to complete the project below. Use the information in the box to help you calculate your answers.

Fun World

Your excellent grades have won you and one classmate a free trip to Fun World. The two of you will have $450 to spend on these special activities. All other activities are included in your admission. You must stay together all day.

Safari Ride	$30/hour
Big Top Mini Circus	$25/hour
Mini Indy 500	$20/hour
"Wide" Water Rafting	$25/hour
See-the-Future Tour	$15/hour
Record-a-Song	$35/hour
Haunted Wax Museum	$10/hour

All special activities last one hour.

The per-hour price stays the same no matter how long you participate.

Fun World's hours of operation are from 9:00 a.m. to 8:00 p.m.

All special activities cease two hours before closing.

a. Are there any activities you could afford to do for the whole day from opening to closing? Explain.

_____

_____

_____

_____

_____

b. If you did every activity once, how many more times could you ride the Mini Indy 500?

_____

_____

c. Would you have enough money to record songs for the whole day during the holiday hours of operation, which are 9:00 a.m. to 7:00 p.m. and include a 20 percent discount? Explain.

_____

_____

_____

_____

_____

Remember

- Read all the information carefully. Then read all the information again when you are ready to calculate and write your answers.
- Read the information as many times as you have to. The more you read it, the better you will understand it.

63. Now write a schedule below detailing your day at Fun World. At the top of the left column write "What We Plan to Do." At the top of the right column write "Time." Be sure to include all the things you plan to do, not just the special rides. At the end, calculate how much of the $450 you will spend, and how much of it, if any, you will have left. Make all decisions together.

UNIT: 4

TESTS ABOUT YOUR SUBJECT AREAS

Subject-area tests generally test your knowledge of different areas you study in school, like science and social studies. Questions on subject-area tests are often asked in multiple-choice form.

PRACTICE MAKES PERFECT

In Unit 1, you learned some strategies for answering multiple-choice questions. Here are some multiple-choice questions in the subject areas of science and social studies. Use the strategies you learned to answer them.

Hints:

When you are not sure of the right choice in multiple-choice questions in science and social studies, try this:

- Use what you do know to find the answers that you can eliminate right away.
- Focus on the remaining ones to make your best choice.

Try It Yourself

Read each item. Then fill in the oval next to the correct response.

Science

1. A person's circulatory system includes_____.

- ◯ a. bones and muscles
- ◯ b. heart and blood
- ◯ c. eyes and ears
- ◯ d. veins and bones

2. Knees, elbows, and ankles are _____.

- ◯ a. joints
- ◯ b. arteries
- ◯ c. muscles
- ◯ d. tissues

3. Breathing is controlled by the body's_____.
○ a. solar system
○ b. skeletal system
○ c. respiratory system
○ d. pancreatic system

4. Your nervous system sends and receives signals from _____.
○ a. your heart
○ b. your lungs
○ c. your veins
○ d. your brain

5. During a sunny winter day, which vehicle would be the warmest to touch?
○ a. a blue car
○ b. a red car
○ c. a white car
○ d. a black car

6. Which of these is not an energy source?
○ a. water
○ b. steel
○ c. oil
○ d. sun

7. The energy source that powers Earth's water condensation cycle is _____.
○ a. Earth's rotation
○ b. heat from the sun
○ c. radiation
○ d. a battery

8. Coal is often referred to as a _____.
○ a. glacier
○ b. purifier
○ c. fossil fuel
○ d. liquid

9. Which is true about oil?
○ a. The United States produces all the world's oil.
○ b. Motor oil and gasoline are refined petroleum.
○ c. Oil is hydrogen and oxygen.
○ d. A pipe cleaner transports oil from Alaska.

10. What is the layer of the atmosphere closest to the Earth called?
○ a. the troposphere
○ b. the mesosphere
○ c. the Greenhouse Effect
○ d. the ionosphere

11. What can you do during the winter to save the most energy?
○ a. Watch less television.
○ b. Lower the thermostat 5°.
○ c. Open the windows.
○ d. Raise the thermostat 5°.

12. Why do scientists continue to search for new ways to conserve fossil fuels?
○ a. Locating fossil fuels is fun.
○ b. Fossil fuels contain dinosaur bones.
○ c. There is an unlimited supply of fossil fuels.
○ d. We may run out of fossil fuels.

Social Studies

13. What is the study of Earth and its features called?
- ○ a. history
- ○ c. psychology
- ○ b. geography
- ○ d. sociology

14. Which of the following statements about a globe is not true?
- ○ a. It is a representation of the Earth.
- ○ b. It shows the shape of land masses more accurately than most maps.
- ○ c. It usually shows lines of longitude and latitude.
- ○ d. It is easier than a map to use when trying to locate specific towns and cities.

Use the following chart for items 15-16.

Population of the 13 colonies around 1700			
New Hampshire	5,000	Delaware	4,000
Massachusetts	56,000	Maryland	43,000
Connecticut	26,000	Virginia	78,000
Rhode Island	6,000	North Carolina	15,000
New York	22,000	South Carolina	11,000
Pennsylvania	24,000	Georgia*	- - - - - - -
New Jersey	20,000		
		*not yet a colony	

15. Which of the 13 colonies had the highest population?
- ○ a. Massachusetts
- ○ b. New York
- ○ c. Virginia
- ○ d. Maryland

16. The population of New Jersey in 1700 was _____ .
- ○ a. greater than that of Pennsylvania
- ○ b. less than that of North Carolina
- ○ c. the same as that of Connecticut
- ○ d. the same as North Carolina's and New Hampshire's combined

Read the statement below, then complete items 17-18.

"Is life so dear, or peace so sweet, as to be purchased at the price of chains and slavery? Forbid it, almighty God! I know not what course others may take; but as for me, give me liberty, or give me death!"

—Patrick Henry

17. Patrick Henry is _____ .
- ○ a. supporting the idea of American liberty
- ○ b. supporting British rule over North America
- ○ c. supporting slavery
- ○ d. disagreeing with freedom of religion

18. Patrick Henry is using slavery as a symbol for _____ .
- ○ a. death
- ○ b. his country's lack of independence
- ○ c. the American Revolution
- ○ d. King George III of England

TESTS WITH DIAGRAMS AND MAPS

Some subject-area tests will check your ability to read maps and diagrams. These types of tests often ask multiple-choice questions that must be answered from information given in a map or diagram.

Here is an example.

Start by looking at this diagram of how the heart works.

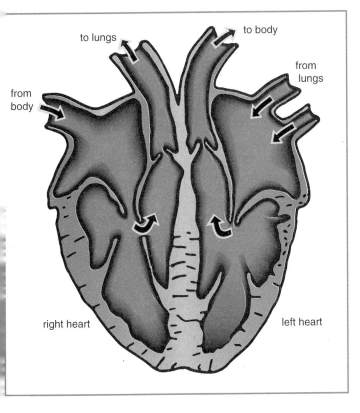

to lungs

to body

from lungs

from body

right heart

left heart

A science test might ask you to use the diagram to choose a word to complete a sentence:

The right part of the heart pumps blood from the body to the _____ .
- ◯ a. brain
- ◯ b. lungs
- ◯ c. liver
- ◯ d. stomach

The part of the diagram labeled *right heart* shows that blood is pumped from the body to the lungs. So you would mark the oval next to *b. lungs.*

Try It Yourself

19. According to the diagram at left, the left part of the heart receives blood from the _____ .
- ◯ a. body
- ◯ b. left heart
- ◯ c. brain
- ◯ d. lungs

(Continue to page 64)

Science

Use the diagram below for items 20-23. Fill in the oval next to the correct response.

Hint:

Before you look at the questions, scan the diagram to get an idea of the type and placement of information there. After you read a question, study the diagram more closely for the specific information you need in order to answer the question.

20. The satellite dish receives signals from _____ .

○ a. a cable
○ b. a broadcast tower
○ c. a communications satellite
○ d. the viewers

21. The cable station transmits its programming to viewers through a _____ .

○ a. wire
○ b. satellite
○ c. satellite dish
○ d. cable

22. A cable station receives broadcast signals from _____.

○ a. a communications satellite and cable
○ b. a cable station
○ c. a satellite dish and broadcast tower
○ d. viewers

23. The diagram shows that the cable station receives programs in _____ .

○ a. two ways
○ b. three ways
○ c. four ways
○ d. five ways

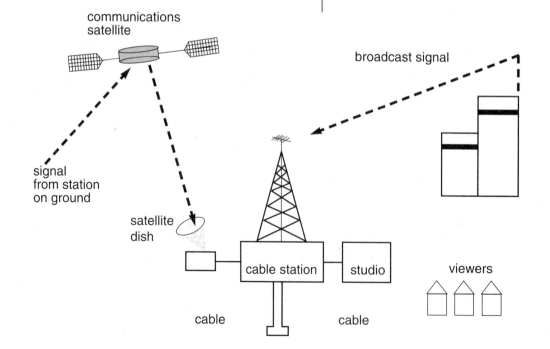

communications satellite

broadcast signal

signal from station on ground

satellite dish

cable station

studio

viewers

cable

cable

Social Studies

Look at the population-density map below. Then complete items 24-27.

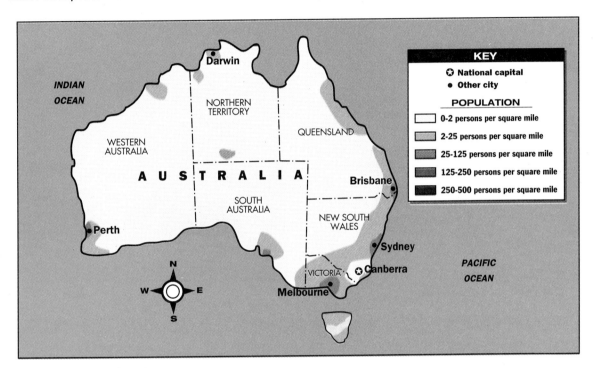

24. Which of the following statements about Australia's population is true?

○ a. Most Australians live in the middle of the country.

○ b. Australia's population is evenly distributed throughout the country.

○ c. Most Australians live in the southeastern part of the country.

○ d. Australia's most-populated cities are in the western half of the country.

25. In most of Australia the population-density range is _____ .

○ a. 250 to 500 people per square mile

○ b. 25 to 125 people per square mile

○ c. 2 to 25 people per square mile

○ d. 0 to 2 people per square mile

26. The second-most-densely populated part of Australia is the _____.

○ a. northern coast

○ b. northwestern coast

○ c. southwestern tip

○ d. central part

27. Which of the following statements is true?

○ a. Canberra is more densely populated than Darwin.

○ b. Brisbane is in a more populated area than Darwin.

○ c. The Northern Territory is a densely populated area.

○ d. New South Wales is one of the least populated areas.

Some subject-area tests will use short-response items to check your ability to read maps and diagrams. On these tests you will be asked to write the correct answer.

Look at this diagram of how a volcanic mountain erupts. A science test might ask you to study the diagram, then write in the correct word to complete this sentence:

The mouth of a volcano is called the

_____.

The diagram shows that the top, or mouth, of the volcano is labeled *crater*. You would write *crater* in the space.

Try It Yourself
Now do these on your own.

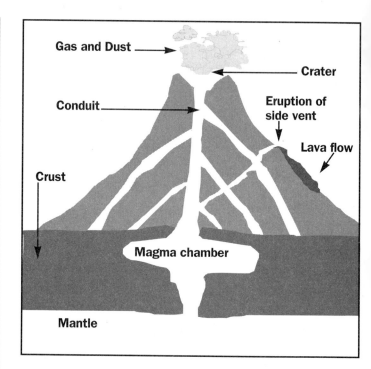

28. What exits through the crater of the volcano? _____

29. In what part of the volcano do eruptions begin? _____

30. Besides the central vent, where else can an eruption take place in a volcano?_____

Use the information on this time line for items 31-33.
Write your responses in the spaces provided.

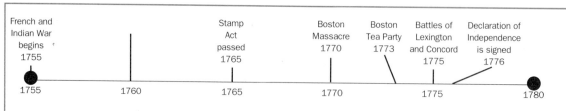

31. Which event happened first on the time line?

_____

32. What happened between the Boston Massacre and the Battles of Lexington and Concord? _____

33. Between what 10 years did most of the events on this time line occur? _____

TESTS WITH WRITING

Subject-area tests may ask you to use different kinds of writing to answer questions about topics you have studied. Sometimes you will be asked to use just facts to describe or present information. Other times you will be asked to use a combination of facts and opinions to express a particular point of view on a topic.

Before you start the test, read the directions and make sure you understand what type of writing you are being asked to do. No matter what type it is, always use complete sentences with correct spelling and punctuation.

A Description or Explanation

One type of report you may be asked to write gives a description or an explanation. In this type of report, your goal is to give information without including your own reactions or feelings.

For example, if you are asked to explain how to housebreak a puppy, you might include:

- the steps to take when training a dog
- the materials needed
- the best time for training

You would probably not include:

- how hard it was to train your dachshund
- whether you like cleaning up after your dog

Try It Yourself

34. Pick a topic for an explanation or description paper. You can choose your own topic or try one of these ideas:

- How to Maintain a Healthy Body
- The Government's System of Checks and Balances
- Small Things You Can Do at Home to Save the Earth

Make a list of three to five things your paper might include.

_____

_____

_____

_____

_____

35. On the back of this page, write a paper on your topic. Use the list you made above to guide you when writing your report.

Writing a Compare-and-Contrast Essay

When you are asked to write an essay that compares or compares and contrasts, you are being asked to say how certain things are alike and how they are different. Here are some steps to follow:

- Be sure you understand what you are supposed to compare and contrast.
- Gather information, either from your subject-area knowledge or from your experience, about the similarities and differences between what you are asked to compare.
- Choose the points you are going to compare.
- Plan how you will organize your comparison. Will you write about one thing and then the other? Or will you compare them point by point?
- Once you make a plan, stick with it.

Imagine that a science test asks you to compare and contrast stratus and cirrus clouds. You might decide that you want to compare what they look like, what they are made of, and where they are located.

Then you might decide you want to write about stratus clouds first and cirrus clouds second.

An outline of this essay might look like this:

A. Introduction

B. Stratus clouds
1. What they look like
2. What they are made of
3. Where they are located

C. Cirrus clouds
1. What they look like
2. What they are made of
3. Where they are located

D. Conclusion

Notice that the same points of comparison are covered in both sections and that, in each section, they are covered in the same order.

Hint:

When you are writing any type of essay, be sure to include an introduction and a conclusion.

- Your introduction should let your reader know what to expect from your essay. This is also where you will want to try to get your readers interested in your topic.
- Your conclusion should provide some sort of closing for your piece of writing. A summary often works well.

36. Make an outline like the one above for an essay that compares reptiles and amphibians. (You may use reference books to help you.)

_____

_____

_____

_____

_____

_____

_____

Hint

- Before you write, think about how you will organize your comparison essay. You can either write about reptiles and then about amphibians, or you can compare them point by point.
- Be sure you discuss the same points for each type of animal. For example, if you are going to mention where reptiles live, also mention where amphibians live.

Try It Yourself

37. In the space below, expand your outline from page 69 into an essay.

from page 69

SUPER TEST-TAKER TIP: REVIEW YOUR WRITTEN WORK

Before submitting your answer to an essay question, ask yourself the following:

- Does my response answer the question that was asked?
- Have I explained my answer clearly?
- Does my essay have a beginning, middle, and end?
- Have I followed the rules of spelling and grammar?

And remember: Make sure you always save time to proofread your writing and, if possible, check the facts.

Writing a Persuasive Essay

The persuasive essay is what you would use to answer a question that asks you to take a position or develop one side of an argument.

Follow these steps when you write a persuasive essay:

- Gather information about your topic. It may come from your experience, books, or other sources.
- Choose your position on the issue.
- Do some prewriting. Write down all the points or reasons that support your position.
- Examine your points and choose the strongest ones.
- Decide the best order in which to present them. You may want to save the strongest point for last.
- Be sure to explain each of your points so that your readers will understand them.

If you are writing that dogs make better pets than cats, you may list as your reasons that dogs are more affectionate, that dogs are more loyal, that dogs can do more tricks, and that dogs are easier to care for. When you review your points, you may want to cross out the last one. It is weak because it is easy to disagree with.

Try It Yourself

38. To help save the rain forests, you want to convince people that rain forests are important to our environment. List on the lines below the most important reasons for saving the rain forests.

_____

_____

_____

_____

_____

39. Put a check mark next to the most persuasive reasons in the list above. Use them to help you write an essay. Put the reasons in the order that will have the most impact.

40. Write your essay on the back of this page.